This edition published by Parragon Books Ltd in 2014

Parragon Books Ltd
Chartist House
15–17 Trim Street
Bath BA1 1HA, UK
www.parragon.com

Written by Frances Prior-Reeves
Designed by Talking Design
Illustrations by Eleanor Carter

ISBN 978-1-4723-5624-6

Printed in China

Oodles of Doodles

PaRragon

Bath · New York · Cologne · Melbourne · Delhi
Hong Kong · Shenzhen · Singapore · Amsterdam

'IN ART, AS THE BEST WAY REMEDY IS TO ADVANTAGE

IN *life,*
TO
mistakes
TAKE
OF THEM.'

Walter Darby Bannard.

Fill this page with *spirals*
what happens when they overlap?

Can you create a whirlpool of colour?

Draw this *bird's song.*

Colour this **PATTERN**, making sure that any segments that touch aren't in the same **COLOUR**.

Draw your **happiest** mood.

Draw your **SADDEST** mood.

Draw your angriest mood.

Draw something tiny.

Draw something

GIGANTIC.

Draw without
RESTRICTIONS.

Draw your

IDEA.

Draw a **target** using only SQUARES.

Draw a brick wall using only
CIRCLES.

What does the colour **GREEN** look like in love?

What does the colour 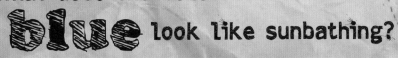 look like sunbathing?

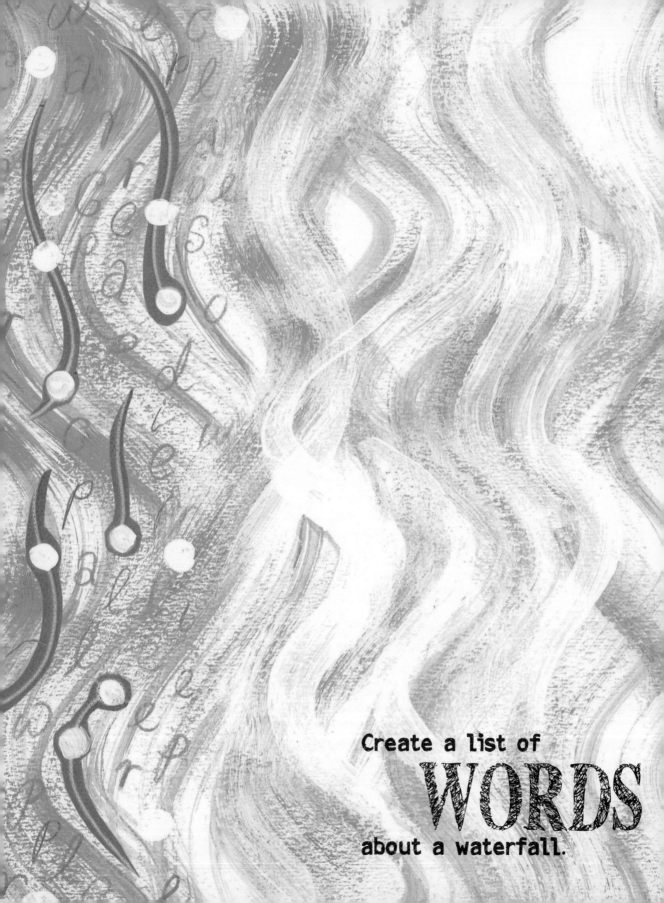

Create a list of

WORDS

about a waterfall.

Flow those words into an IMAGE.

Draw your favourite **song**.

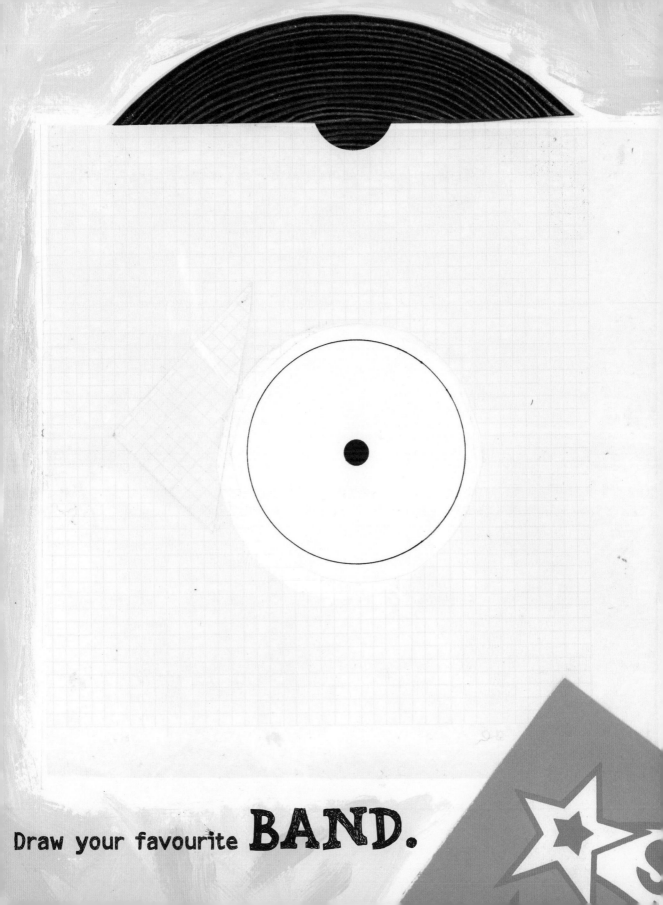

Draw your favourite **BAND.**

Draw an **animal** that combines your *five favourite* animals.

'If you hear
you say " you
then by all
and that voice

a voice within
cannot paint",
means paint,
will be silenced.'

Vincent Van Gogh.

Doodles
don't have to
be mindless.

Draw a portrait of yourself in **disguise.**

Draw a portrait of **yourself**
with your *eyes closed.*

Draw the thing that goes BUMP in the night.

BE
CREATIVE!

Draw a **Jealous** colour.

Draw a **calm** colour.

Draw PURPLE and yellow in love.

Draw once upon a time.

Fill these pages with shapes with more than **FIVE SIDES.**

Draw a *mirage*.

'I found I could say things with colour and shapes that I couldn't say any other way - things I had no words for.'

Georgia O'Keeffe.

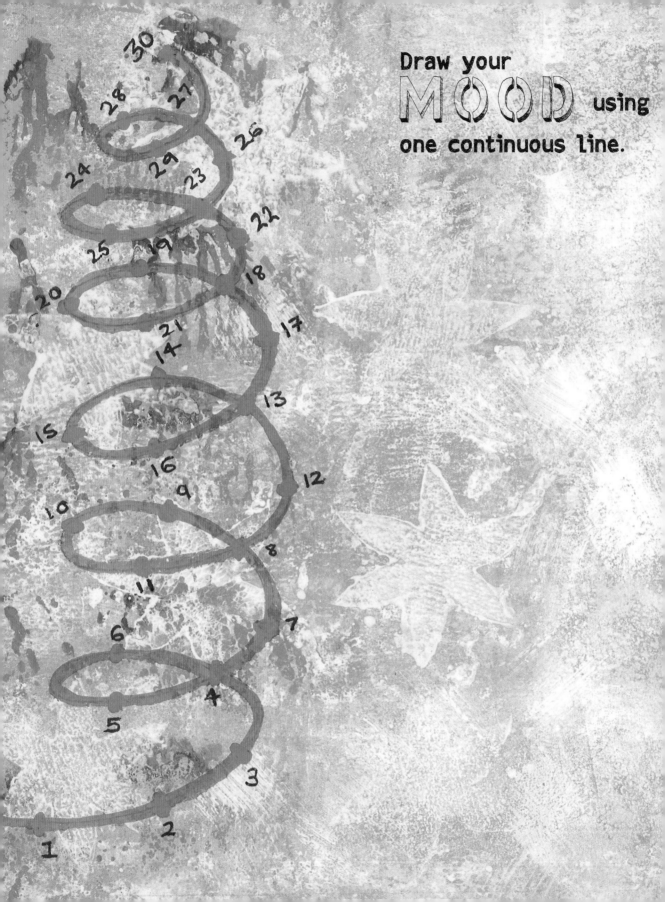

Draw your **MOOD** using one continuous line.

Colour!

Fill this grassland with *life.*

sown closely in beds (or boxes) and to fill in any blanks that

Draw the day you've just had.

Create a pattern using different types of STARS.

Space for your
creativity.

Draw your favourite BOOK.

Draw your favourite SERIES.

Draw something HAIRY.

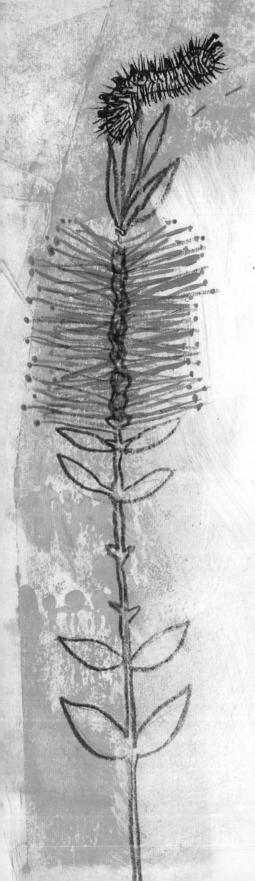

SHADE these pages and then use a rubber to cut through it and create something beneath.

Create a list of **words** about the **rainforest.**

Grow those words into an

image.

Draw a reflection in this
PUDDLE.

Fill this *night sky* with stars.

SCRIBBLE!

Draw a **striped spot.**

Draw a **SPOTTED STRIPE.**

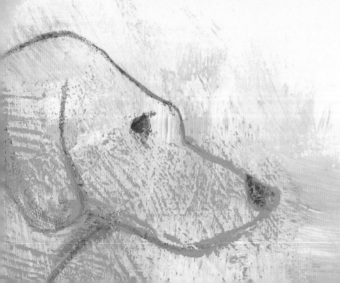

Draw a striped dalmation.

Draw a spotted TIGER.

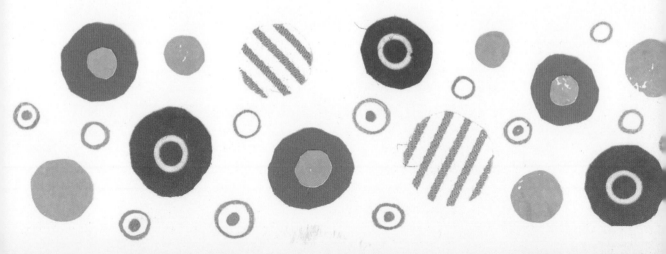

Personalize this space.

Look around and pick out
everything
that is blue.

Draw *everything* you

see in that colour in

ONE PICTURE.

Draw a *windy day.*

Draw something **WIDE.**

Draw something NARROW.

'Think left and
and think low
Oh, the thinks
up if only you

think right
and think high.
you can think
try.'
Dr. Seuss.

Draw a
DIAMOND
spinning.

Draw a *ZIGZAG* waving.

Draw a **triangle** doing cartwheels.

Draw a **GEOMETRIC**

TESSELLATING pattern.

Draw the *view*
from your
window.

Draw the view from

OUTSIDE

your window

looking in.

Create a new **font** that shows your *personal* style.

C O T J

Y f S X

Drawing is creating!

Assign **MOODS** to each colour.

If you **INVERT** these what would happen to the mood of a picture?

'I've been 40 years discovering that the queen of all colours was black.'

Pierre-Auguste Renoir.

Draw your happiest memory.

Draw something shiny.

Sketch!

Add a row of **exotic birds**
to this branch in BLACK AND WHITE.

Draw a **CHESSBOARD,** *piano* and a **newspaper** using only primary colours.

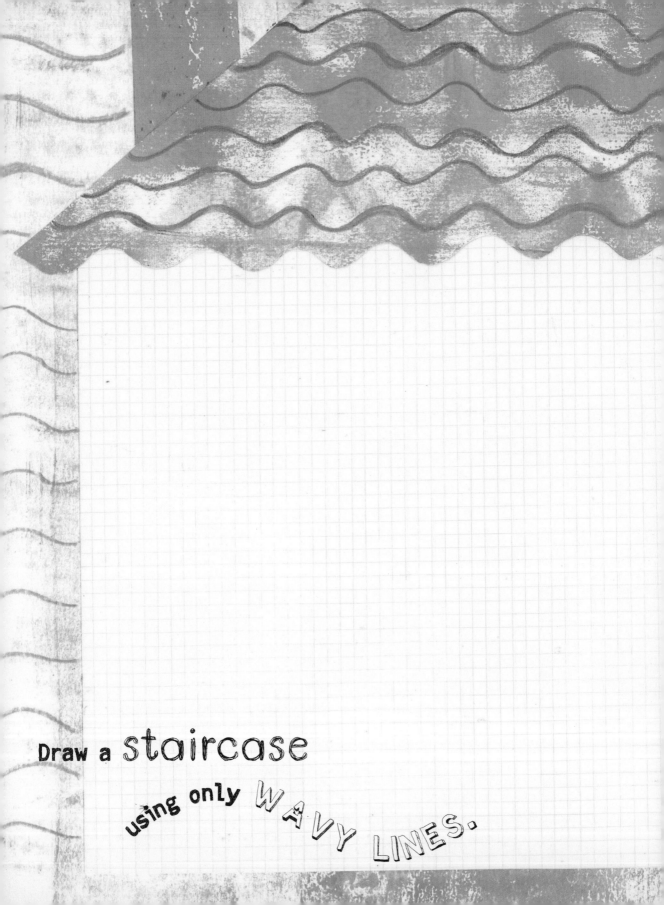

Draw a staircase

using only WAVY LINES.

Draw the **sea** using only diagonal lines.

Draw what's **directly in front** of you using one continuous line.

Create a list of words about

CLOUDS.

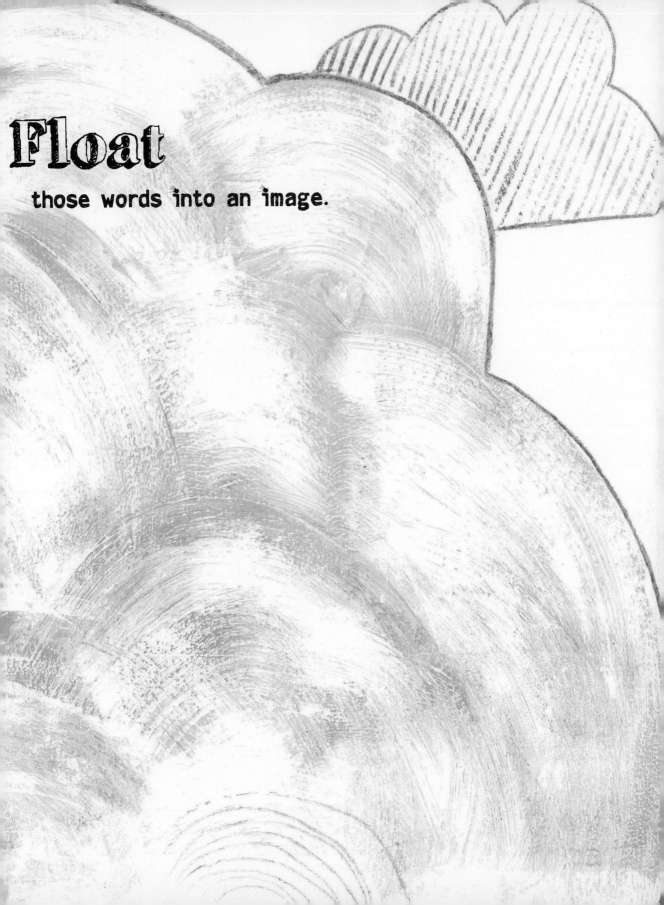

Float

those words into an image.

Draw an ANT the size of a house.

Draw an **oak tree** the size of a grass seed.

Draw a **bird in a tree** in BLUE and *green* tones.

Draw a **bird in a tree** in
red and **ORANGE** tones.

What changes?

'Creativity is
INTELLIGENCE
having fun.'

Albert Einstein.

Draw the ending to your **adventure story** here.

Fill this page with a night-time
CITYSCAPE.

Draw your favourite TV Programme.

Draw your favourite

FILM.

DON'T THINK JUST DRAW.

Draw a *portrait* of yourself from the back.

Draw a portrait of yourself upside down.

Draw what is at the **BOTTOM** of this well.

Draw something **you're looking forward to.**

Light a
campfire.

Draw the **SMOKE** billowing on to this page.

Look around and pick
out everything that is

RED.

Draw everything you
 see in that **colour**
in one picture.

Draw something
that begins with
the letter

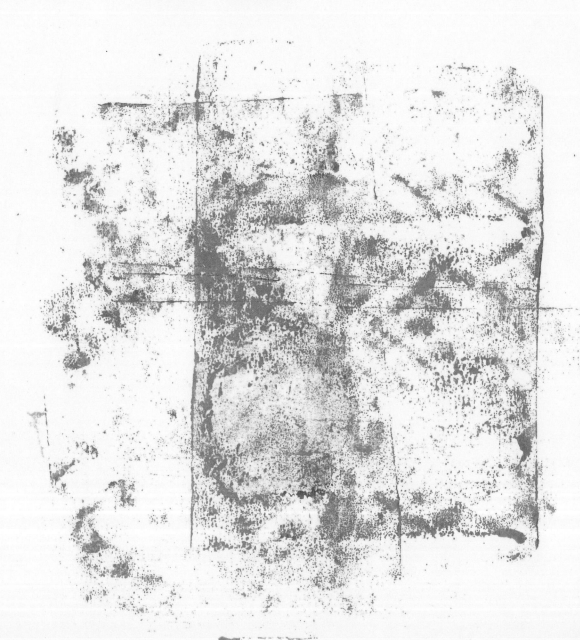

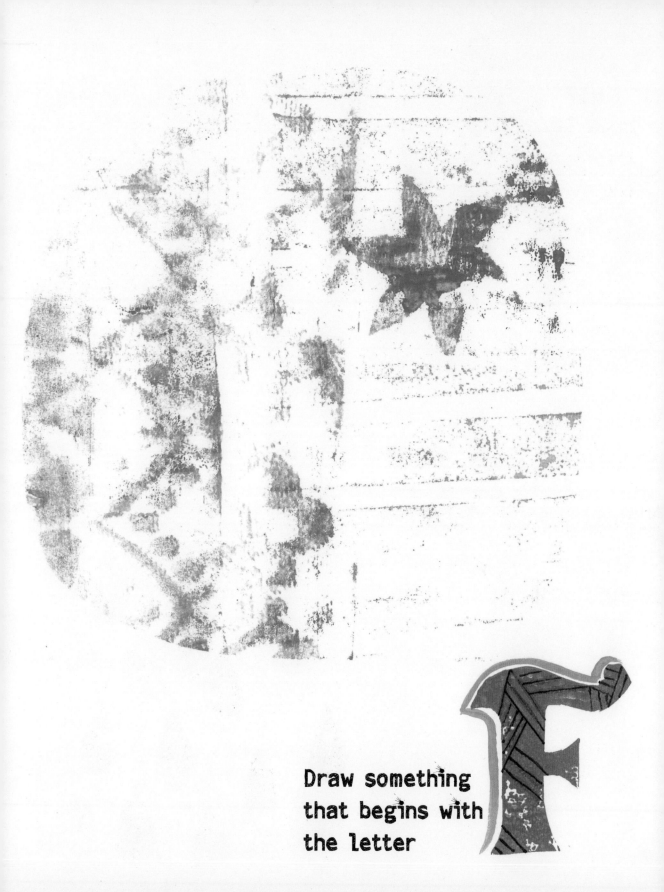

Draw something
that begins with
the letter

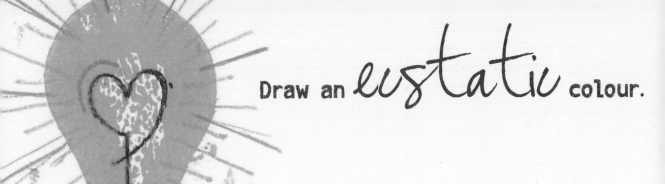

Draw an *ecstatic* colour.

Draw a SAD colour.

Draw PINK and RED in a fight.

CREATE!

Fill THESE PAGES with as many ideas as you can ...